GOSCINNY AND UDERZO

PRESENT

An Asterix Adventure

ASTERIX
AND THE
GOLDEN SICKLE

Written by RENÉ GOSCINNY *and Illustrated by* ALBERT UDERZO

Translated by Anthea Bell *and* Derek Hockridge

Orion
Children's Books

Asterix titles available now

ORION CHILDREN'S BOOKS

This revised edition first published in 2004 by Orion Books Ltd
This edition published in 2016 by Hodder and Stoughton

19 20

ASTERIX®-OBELIX®-DOGMATIX®
© 1962 GOSCINNY/UDERZO
Revised edition and English translation © 2004 Hachette Livre
Original title: *La Serpe d'or*
Exclusive licensee: Hachette Children's Group
Translators: Anthea Bell and Derek Hockridge
Typography: Bryony Newhouse

The right of René Goscinny and Albert Uderzo to be identified as the authors of this work
has been asserted by them in accordance with the Copyright, Designs and Patents Act 1988.

A CIP record for this book is available from the British Library

ISBN 978-0-7528-6612-3 (cased)
ISBN 978-0-7528-6613-0 (paperback)
ISBN 978-1-4440-1309-2 (ebook)

Orion Children's Books
An imprint of Hachette Children's Group, part of Hodder and Stoughton
Carmelite House, 50 Victoria Embankment
London EC4Y 0DZ
An Hachette UK Company

www.hachette.co.uk
www.asterix.com
www.hachettechildrens.co.uk

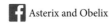 Asterix and Obelix

BELGICA

GAULISH VILLAGE

COMPENDIUM

LAUDANUM

AQUARIUM

TOTORUM

ARMORICA

LUTETIA

GAUL
(ROMAN CONQUEST)
50 BC

CELTICA

AQUITANIA

PROVINCIA

THE YEAR IS 50 BC. GAUL IS ENTIRELY OCCUPIED BY THE
ROMANS. WELL, NOT ENTIRELY ... ONE SMALL VILLAGE OF
INDOMITABLE GAULS STILL HOLDS OUT AGAINST THE INVADERS.
AND LIFE IS NOT EASY FOR THE ROMAN LEGIONARIES WHO
GARRISON THE FORTIFIED CAMPS OF TOTORUM, AQUARIUM,
LAUDANUM AND COMPENDIUM ...

ASTERIX, THE HERO OF THESE ADVENTURES. A SHREWD, CUNNING LITTLE WARRIOR, ALL PERILOUS MISSIONS ARE IMMEDIATELY ENTRUSTED TO HIM. ASTERIX GETS HIS SUPERHUMAN STRENGTH FROM THE MAGIC POTION BREWED BY THE DRUID GETAFIX . . .

OBELIX, ASTERIX'S INSEPARABLE FRIEND. A MENHIR DELIVERY MAN BY TRADE, ADDICTED TO WILD BOAR. OBELIX IS ALWAYS READY TO DROP EVERYTHING AND GO OFF ON A NEW ADVENTURE WITH ASTERIX – SO LONG AS THERE'S WILD BOAR TO EAT, AND PLENTY OF FIGHTING. HIS CONSTANT COMPANION IS DOGMATIX, THE ONLY KNOWN CANINE ECOLOGIST, WHO HOWLS WITH DESPAIR WHEN A TREE IS CUT DOWN.

GETAFIX, THE VENERABLE VILLAGE DRUID, GATHERS MISTLETOE AND BREWS MAGIC POTIONS. HIS SPECIALITY IS THE POTION WHICH GIVES THE DRINKER SUPERHUMAN STRENGTH. BUT GETAFIX ALSO HAS OTHER RECIPES UP HIS SLEEVE . . .

CACOFONIX, THE BARD. OPINION IS DIVIDED AS TO HIS MUSICAL GIFTS. CACOFONIX THINKS HE'S A GENIUS. EVERYONE ELSE THINKS HE'S UNSPEAKABLE. BUT SO LONG AS HE DOESN'T SPEAK, LET ALONE SING, EVERYBODY LIKES HIM . . .

FINALLY, VITALSTATISTIX, THE CHIEF OF THE TRIBE. MAJESTIC, BRAVE AND HOT-TEMPERED, THE OLD WARRIOR IS RESPECTED BY HIS MEN AND FEARED BY HIS ENEMIES. VITALSTATISTIX HIMSELF HAS ONLY ONE FEAR, HE IS AFRAID THE SKY MAY FALL ON HIS HEAD TOMORROW. BUT AS HE ALWAYS SAYS, TOMORROW NEVER COMES.

THE FIERCELY INDEPENDENT LITTLE VILLAGE WHERE ASTERIX AND THE OTHER GAULS LIVE IS AT PEACE...

GOOD HUNTING, ASTERIX?

NOTHING MUCH TODAY...

OBELIX IS HAPPILY AT WORK, CARVING OUT A MENHIR...

THERE'LL ALWAYS BE A GAU-AAUL...

CACOFONIX THE BARD IS GIVING THE CHILDREN LESSONS...

WELL, YOUNG MAN, AND INTO HOW MANY PARTS IS GAUL DIVIDED?

?

$$VIII \times V = XL$$
$$\frac{III}{+ I} = IV$$

IN SHORT, EVERYONE IS CONTENTED. ALL IS PEACE AND PLENTY...

ANOTHER BOAR, OBELIX?

YES, PLEASE!

WHEN SUDDENLY...

OH, BY TOUTATIS!

??

?

?

?

7

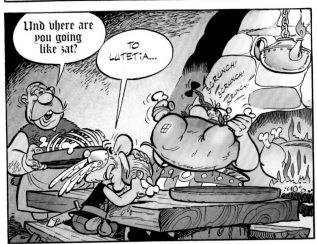

NEXT MORNING...

Auf wiedersehen!

The Cont Barbaria

HEY, ASTERIX, WHY DO YOU THINK THAT TRAVELLER TOLD US SICKLES WERE IN SHORT SUPPLY IN LUTETIA?

NO IDEA, OBELIX.

LET'S ENJOY OUR JOURNEY; WE CAN WORRY ABOUT THAT LATER...

THE ROMANS ARE RUINING THE LANDSCAPE WITH ALL THESE MODERN BUILDINGS!

OUR FRIENDS' JOURNEY PROCEEDS WITHOUT MUCH INCIDENT, APART FROM A FEW SCUFFLES WITH BANDITS...

AT SUINDINUM, ASTERIX AND OBELIX ARE UNABLE TO FIND A BED, AS IT HAPPENS TO BE THE DAY OF THE GREAT OX-CART RACE, THE SUINDINUM 24 HOURS...

BUT AT LAST, ONE DAY...

LOOK! OBELIX!

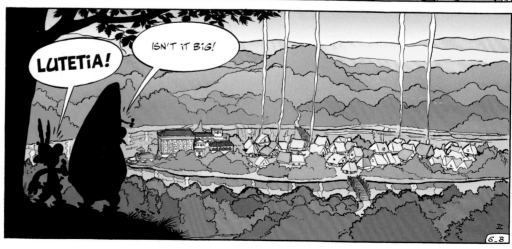

LUTETIA!

ISN'T IT BIG!

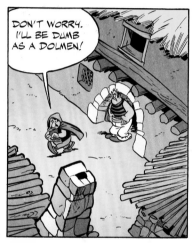

15

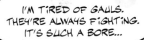

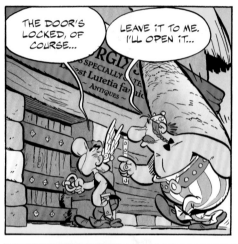

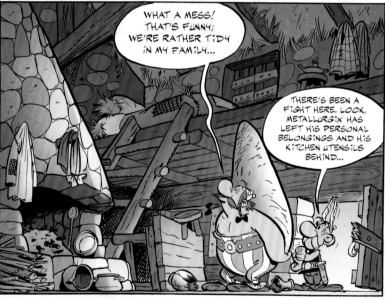

THE SUN, RISING ON LUTETIA, IS GREETED BY A COCKEREL...

COCK-A-DOODLE-DO!

GET UP, OBELIX! IT'S TIME TO START OUR INVESTIGATIONS!

THAT'S RIGHT. WE MUST FIND METALLURGIX.

LET'S GO BACK TO THAT ARVERNIAN IN THE WINE SHOP. I'M SURE HE KNOWS SOMETHING!

THE SUN OF MASSILIA

OH!

COULD YOU TELL US WHERE TO FIND THE ARVERNIAN WHO...

OH, I EXPECT YOU MEAN THE FORMER PROPRIETOR?

THAT CRAZY GAUL WHO SOLD ME THIS PLACE FOR A HANDFUL OF BRONZE COINS! IT'S UNDER NEW MANAGEMENT NOW, BUT YOU WON'T BE DISAPPOINTED!

I CAN OFFER YOU MY SPECIALITY: FISH SOUP! MADE OF NICE FRESH FISH, JUST ARRIVED BY OX-CART FROM MASSILIA!

DO YOU KNOW WHERE THE ARVERNIAN HAS GONE?

OH! HE STARTED FOR GERGOVIA THIS MORNING, TRAVELLING BY OX-CART, THE SAME AS THE FISH!

THE SUN OF MASSILIA

WHAT A SHAME! IF YOU'D COME A LITTLE SOONER YOU'D HAVE FOUND HIM STILL HERE!

THANKS!

ALL THESE LUTETIANS ARE CRAZY, BY BELISAMA!

LONG LIVE VERCINGE... HIC! ... TORIX!

HELLO. WHAT ARE YOU INSIDE FOR? HIC!

WE'RE LOOKING FOR A MAN CALLED CLOVOGARLIX...

(SIGH)

I KNOW HIM. HE... HIC! ...USHED TO WORK AT NAVISHTRIX'S PLACE!

NAVISHTRIX HAD A LOVELY LITTLE WINE FROM GALLIA NARBONENSIS... HIC! ...LOVELY LITTLE WINE... ALL DONE FOR NOW... HIC! .....ALL OVER!

IT'SH SAD... SAAAAD! BOOHOO... HIC! ...HOOOOO...

ANY IDEA WHERE NAVISHTRIX AND CLOVOGARLIX MIGHT HAVE GONE?

NO... SNIFF! ...BUT I OFTEN HEARD THEM ARRANGING TO MEET UNDER THE DOLMEN... HIC!

UNDER THE DOLMEN?

IT'S A CLUE. ONLY A SLIGHT CLUE, BUT A CLUE! LET'S GET OUT OF HERE!

RIGHT.

CRAAASH!

?

LONG LIVE VERGINCE... VERCEGIN... HIC! ...VERCEGINTORIX!

22

WARM RAYS OF BRILLIANT SUNSHINE LIGHT UP A CLOUDLESS SKY...

...LITTLE BIRDS WARBLE ON THE LEAFY BRANCHES...

...SQUIRRELS PLAY ON THE MOSSY GROUND..

...WHILE UNDERNEATH THE MOSSY GROUND..

GET THEM, OBELIX!

YOU BET I WILL, ASTERIX!

BOING PLAF! OUCH! BOUM!

ARE THERE ANY LEFT, ASTERIX?

NO, OBELIX, YOU'RE JUST FINISHING OFF THE LAST ONE...

BONG! BONG! BONG!

LET'S GET OUT OF HERE AND WARN THE BOSS!

OBELIX, I'M A BIT WORRIED... I CAN'T FIND NAVISHTRIX!

HE CAN'T HAVE COME TO ANY HARM. HE WAS HERE JUST NOW!

ANYWAY, I'VE GOT CLOVOGARLIX.

THAT'S SOMETHING...

31

YOU LOT, HOP IT! WE WON'T NEED YOU ANY MORE!

WHAT HAPPENED? WOULD SOMEONE PLEASE ENLIGHTEN ME?

NOT YOU. YOU'VE GOT SOME TALKING TO DO!

I WILL TELL YOU NOTHING!

RIGHT! OFF YOU GO, OBELIX!

I'LL TELL YOU EVERYTHING!

I DON'T KNOW A GREAT DEAL. THIS IS JUST AN UNDERGROUND STORE FOR THE SICKLES. METALLURGIX MADE THEM, AND NAVISHTRIX USED TO BRING THEM HERE...

MY COUSIN METALLURGIX! WHERE'S METALLURGIX?

THE BIG BOSS IS KEEPING HIM PRISONER!

SO NAVISHTRIX ISN'T THE BIG BOSS?

NO, BUT NAVISHTRIX IS THE ONLY ONE WHO KNOWS HIS IDENTITY. BY TOUTATIS, MAY THE SKY FALL ON MY HEAD IF I TELL A LIE!

LET'S GO AND TRY TO FIND THIS BIG BOSS!

RIGHT!

WHAT ABOUT ME? WHAT ARE YOU GOING TO DO WITH ME?

YOU STAY HERE TO LOOK AFTER THE SICKLES. THEY BELONG TO METALLURGIX!

OF COURSE! WITH PLEASURE!

POOR STUPID FOOLS! AS SOON AS THEIR BACKS ARE TURNED, I'LL BE OFF WITH THE SICKLES!

SOON AFTERWARDS...

THIS STONE OVER THE TRAPDOOR WILL HELP OUR FRIEND CLOVOGARLIX OVERCOME TEMPTATION...

HE DOES KNOW SOME NASTY SWEAR WORDS!

1-61

32

36

BY APOLLO! YOU AGAIN!

I COULD SAY THE SAME THING, ROMAN!

?

GRAB HOLD OF THESE TWO MEN!!!

LOOK HERE, BE REASONABLE...

SHALL WE GET THEM, ASTERIX?

NO, OBELIX. I'M SURE WE SHALL BE ABLE TO EXPLAIN EVERYTHING.

WHAT ABOUT MY PRIME STEAK? WHO'S GOING TO PAY FOR MY PRIME STEAK?

SOON AFTERWARDS...

AVE, CENTURION! I'VE BROUGHT IN TWO GAULS!

BY ALL THE GODS, THOSE TWO AGAIN!

WHAT ABOUT MY PRIME...

LISTEN, ROMAN, WE CAN EXPLAIN EVERYTHING...

...STEAK!

NOT A WORD! PUT THEM IN CHAINS AND LOCK THEM UP SEPARATELY!

AND JUST WHAT ARE YOU GOING TO DO ABOUT MY PRIME STEAK?

I'LL SHOW YOU WHAT I'M GOING TO DO ABOUT YOUR PRIME STEAK!!

LATER...

DID YOU CATCH THE THIEF?

NO! GIVE ME A NICE STEAK!

34

44

WITH THEIR GOLDEN SICKLE AT LAST, OUR TWO FRIENDS LEAVE LUTETIA FOR AN UNEVENTFUL JOURNEY...

I LOVE LUTETIA IN THE SPRINGTIME

APART FROM A FEW RASH BANDITS...

I TELL YOU, THE SKY HAS FALLEN ON OUR HEADS!

...A FEW FOOLHARDY BARBARIANS...

Zat vos kein nice zink to do!

Nein, it nicht vos!

COME ALONG, OBELIX! DON'T DAWDLE!

...AND SEVERAL CARELESS WILD BOAR...

...THEIR JOURNEY, AS WE SAID, WAS UNEVENTFUL!

LOOK, OBELIX, THERE'S OUR VILLAGE!

GREAT!

COME ON, EVERYONE! ASTERIX AND OBELIX ARE BACK!

THEY'LL BE ABLE TO TELL US WHAT'S BEING WORN IN LUTETIA THIS SEASON!

WELCOME BACK, BRAVE WARRIORS!

I WILL NOW COMPOSE AN ODE FOR THIS GLORIOUS OCCASION!

JUST YOU TRY IT!

HERE IS YOUR GOLDEN SICKLE, O DRUID GETAFIX!

THANK YOU, MY FRIENDS. I KNEW YOU WOULDN'T FAIL ME!

ALL OUR FRIENDS GATHER TOGETHER FOR A GREAT FEAST TO CELEBRATE THE RETURN OF THE HEROES WITH THE BEAUTIFUL GOLDEN SICKLE WHICH WILL BRING GLORY AND FAME TO THE VILLAGE...

THAT'S FUNNY. OUR BARD CACOFONIX HASN'T TURNED UP TO SING US ONE OF HIS ODES!

HMMM! HMMMM!

THE END

2- 61